How will you create something beautiful together?

To Janet, my best friend, my hero, my wife. From Steve Potter

ACKNOWLEDGEMENTS

The quotations in this book were gathered lovingly but unscientifically over several years and/or were contributed by many friends or acquaintances. Some arrived – and survived in our files – on scraps of paper and may therefore be imperfectly worded or attributed. To the authors, contributors and original sources, our thanks, and where appropriate, our apologies. ~The Editors

WITH SPECIAL THANKS TO

Jason Aldrich, Gerry Baird, Jay Baird, Neil Beaton, Josie Bissett, Laura Boro, Melissa Carlson, Jim and Alyssa Darragh & Family, Sarah Forster, Michael J. Hedge, Liz Heinlein & Family, Renee Holmes, Jennifer Hurwitz, Heidi Jones, Sheila Kamuda, Carol Anne Kennedy, June Martin, Carin Moore, Jessica Phoenix and Tom DesLongchamp, Janet Potter & Family, Heidi & Jose Rodriguez, Diane Roger, Alie Satterlee, Kirsten and Garrett Sessions, Andrea Shirley, Heidi Yamada & Family, Justi and Tote Yamada & Family, Bob and Val Yamada, Kaz and Kristin Yamada & Family, Tai and Joy Yamada, Anne Zadra, August and Arline Zadra, Gus Zadra and Rosie Zadra.

Credits

Written by Dan Zadra and Kobi Yamada; Edited by M.H. Clark; Designed by Steve Potter.

Printed in China

From the time we are very small, we know that one plus one is two. But when the right people come together, one plus one is actually more than two. Much more.

We are not made to go through life alone. Everything about us is designed to become stronger, happier, and more fulfilled when we have found our love, our partner, our matching puzzle piece.

LIFE IS MEANT TO BE SHARED

The miracle is that sharing life actually makes life bigger. The arithmetic is magic. Real love always adds, it never subtracts. With love, we double our joys, divide our worries, and multiply our possibilities for a life of meaning, romance and adventure.

Yes, life was meant to be shared. It's not what we have in our life, but who we have in our life that counts. If you have found love, you have been given life's greatest gift. How will you celebrate it? How will you use it to grow?

How will you create something beautiful together?

**Then we
sat on the edge
of the earth, with our
feet dangling over the
side, and marveled
that we had found
each other.**

~Erick Dillard

Houses, stocks and jewels are nice. But remember to celebrate again and again the beautiful things that money can't buy: a hand in yours; shared dreams; purpose and meaning; friendship and laughter. And a true companion.

We are most alive when our hearts are conscious of our treasures. ~Thornton Wilder

Celebrating Two

Some people never find love. If you have found it, be conscious of your treasure. Marvel at the perfect set of circumstances that conspired to help you find each other.

Pick a time to sit side by side with this book, celebrating two, and looking out at the future together.

There are only four questions of value in life...

What is sacred?

Of what is the spirit made?

What is worth living for,

And what is worth dying for?

The answer to each is the same:

ONLY
LOVE.

~from the movie, Don Juan DeMarco

"An enjoyable disorder characterized

by feelings of excitement, anticipation,

high hopes, recent memories of

interludes, giddiness, and physical

overstimulation which occur

simultaneously when experiencing

Smitten!

a new love. These feelings take over

without warning and make it difficult to

concentrate on anything but romance.

They interfere with work and safe

driving, but should be experienced at

least once in every person's lifetime."

~Urban Dictionary, definition of "twitterpated"

I climbed up the door, and opened the stairs,
I said my pajamas, and put on my prayers,
I turned off the bed and crawled into the light,
And all because you kissed me good-night.

~Eddie Pola

. . . .

. . . .

. . . .

. . . .

. . . .

When was
the moment
you knew?

. . . .

. . . .

. . . .

. . . .

. . . .

. . . .

. . . .

. . . .

. . . .

We is wo

nderful.

I ONLY WISH YOU COULD SEE WHAT I SEE WHEN I LOOK AT YOU.

IT'S OFTEN SAID THAT LOVE IS BLIND, BUT THAT'S NOT REALLY TRUE. WILLIAM SHAKESPEARE HAD IT RIGHT WHEN HE WROTE, "LOVE ADDS A PRECIOUS SEEING TO THE EYE." LOVE IS THE ONLY THING THAT LETS US SEE ALL THE POSSIBILITIES OF LIFE AND EACH OTHER WITH CRYSTAL CLARITY. WITH IT, WE CAN LOOK BEYOND OUR LOVED ONE'S APPARENT LIMITATIONS AND SEE THE GIFTS AND POSSIBILITIES THAT NO ONE ELSE HAD SEARCHED QUITE LONG ENOUGH TO FIND. RATHER THAN SEEKING IMPERFECTIONS AND SHORTCOMINGS, LOVE KEEPS WATCH FOR SIGNS OF LIGHT AND STRENGTH. IT SEES HOW FAR YOUR LOVED ONE HAS COME, NOT HOW FAR HE OR SHE STILL HAS TO GO. LOVE HELPS US DISCOVER QUALITIES IN OURSELVES THAT WE DIDN'T EVEN KNOW WE HAD. WITH LOVE WE CAN FEED EACH OTHER'S DREAMS AND ASPIRATIONS AND, IN THAT WAY, WE CAN EVEN SEE THE FUTURE.

THE WAY I SEE YOU...

Is it Real?

"What is REAL?" asked the Rabbit one day, when they were lying side by side near the nursery fender, before Nana came to tidy the room. "Does it mean having things that buzz inside you and a stick-out handle?"

"Real isn't how you are made," said the Skin Horse. "It's a thing that happens to you. When a child loves you for a long, long time, not just to play with, but really loves you, then you become Real."

"Does it hurt?" asked the Rabbit.

"Sometimes," said the Skin Horse, for he was always truthful. "When you are Real you don't mind being hurt."

"Does it happen all at once, like being wound up," he asked, "or bit by bit?"

"It doesn't happen all at once," said the Skin Horse. "You become. It takes a long time. That's why it doesn't often happen to people who break easily, or have sharp edges, or who have to be carefully kept.

Generally, by the time you are Real, most of your hair has been loved off, and your eyes drop out and you get loose in the joints and very shabby. But these things don't matter at all, because once you are Real, you can't be ugly except to people who don't understand."

~Margery Williams, *The Velveteen Rabbit*

*To see coming toward you the face that
will mean an end of oneness is—far more
than birth itself—the beginning of life.*

~Holly Roth

What makes you happy?

What is your favorite place?

What delights you?

What makes you feel good?

The more I wonder

What do you wonder about?

What is your greatest passion?

What is your most cherished memory?

What do you need to feel safe?

...the more I love.

~Alice Walker

Two halves
have little choice
but to join; and
yes, they do
make a whole.
But two wholes
when they
coincide...that
is beauty.
That is love.

~Lillian Darr

The Love Story of Robert and Elizabeth Barrett Browning

The romance between Robert Browning and Elizabeth Barrett is legendary. No couple has ever written of unconditional love more eloquently or sincerely, or provided a more beautiful example of it in their own lives. When they met, she was 38—a frail and lonely but incredibly gifted poet. A spinal injury had left her in a wheelchair from the age of 15. He was only 32, and a handsome worldly English author.

For the first two years of their courtship, Elizabeth could not believe that Robert really loved her as much as he professed. She thought it was just her poetry that captured his heart. With patience and poetry of his own, he finally convinced her that his love for her was complete. Early in the relationship he wrote to her saying that he loved her poetry with all his heart, but loved her even more. Elizabeth responded in her most famous poem to the man who loved and accepted her unconditionally:

How Do I Love Thee?

How do I love thee? Let me count the ways.
I love thee to the depth and breadth and height
My soul can reach, when feeling out of sight
For the ends of Being and ideal Grace.
I love thee to the level of everyday's
Most quiet need, by sun and candle-light.
I love thee freely, as men strive for Right;
I love thee purely, as they turn from Praise.
I love thee with a passion put to use
In my old griefs, and with my childhood's faith.
I love thee with a love I seemed to lose
With my lost saints—I love thee with the breath,
Smiles, tears, of all my life!—and, if God choose,
I shall but love thee better after death.

Sonnet XLIII
Elizabeth Barrett Browning

Virtually all of the most admired and enduring companies have proclaimed a clear and exciting purpose in the world—their "Corporate Mission Statement." When employees come together to pursue a worthwhile mission (rather than just a job), they feel inspired and united.

The same is true for couples. Some of the happiest and most enduring couples have taken the time to write down their most important values, beliefs, passions and priorities—their guiding stars—and then converted them into a "Couples Mission Statement." From that day forward, their Mission Statement helps guide their most important decisions…and is one of the surest ways to live happily ever after.

Create Your

The Coca-Cola company has been on a mission for more than 100 years. Here's how they express their special purpose in the world:

"Everything we do is inspired by our enduring mission:

To Refresh the World...
in body, mind, and spirit.
To Inspire Moments of Optimism...
through our brands and actions.
To Create Value and Make a Difference...
everywhere we engage."

Mission Statement
If you want to go fast, go alone. If you want to go far, go together. *~African Proverb*

It can be difficult to just sit down and whip out a meaningful Mission Statement together. But it's easy and fun to write if you simply discuss and agree on the following questions first. Once you have the answers to these questions, just string them together, edit them to the shortest and most inspiring combination of words—and your Couples Mission Statement will almost magically materialize.

How to Create Your Couples Mission Statement (the easy way)

What are our top 5-7 values, in order of priority? (From now on, let those top values guide your most important choices and decisions together.)

As a couple, we are strongest when we…

We will try to eliminate times when we…

We will find more time for each other to…

We will support and encourage each other by…

We will make a difference for others by…

We affirm that we will fill our relationship with…

We will constantly refresh and renew ourselves and our relationship by…

Our Mission Statement

Just put your Mission into words and your heart will take it from there.

How to Bring
a Dream to Life

*Every heart has a hidden treasure. A secret
wish. A silent dream. A special goal to long for.*

~Jill Wolf

"Some people call it 'treasure-mapping.'
Six years ago we sat down with some old
magazines, and spent the afternoon cutting out
pictures of places and things that reminded us
of our shared dreams. Then we glued them into
a collage that helped us to visualize what we
really wanted out of our life together.

"Our collage showed a big log house on a hill,
with a beautiful lake in the background, a barn
and some horses in a pasture, and a garden
with fruit trees. The picture kept us on track
over the years. Now, when we watch the cherry
trees break into bloom every spring, we can
hardly believe this collage became the very life
we wake up to each morning."

Instructions: Grab a pile of magazines and start cutting out pictures and headlines that help you clearly visualize one of your most exciting dreams—something you most want to do, have, be, see, or achieve together. Hang this visual image in your kitchen or bedroom—somewhere where you can gaze at it regularly together. Don't worry about how you are actually going to make the dream come true. The simple act of converting your dream into a visual "image" has an uncanny way of stimulating your creativity— and the "how" will eventually open up to you.

Picture a dream together, and then live toward it.

Life is a Shared Adventure

Anything, everything, little or big becomes an adventure when the right person shares it. ~Kathleen Norris

Amazing things start happening when you simply give yourselves permission to finish this phrase: "I've always wanted to…"

Fill in the blank with some adventure or activity that one of you has always wanted to try—and then make it happen together.

I'VE ALWAYS WANTED TO BACKPACK THROUGH INDIA LEARN TO SPEAK FRENCH RAFT THE COLORADO RIVER LIVE ON A HOUSEBOAT FOR A SUMMER QUIT MY JOB AND OPEN A CERAMICS SHOP TRACE MY ANCESTRY TAKE FLYING LESSONS RUN A HALF-MARATHON TEACH SOMEONE TO READ BUILD A TREEHOUSE SLEEP OUT UNDER THE STARS GROW AN HERB GARDEN COOK A THREE-COURSE MEAL FROM SCRATCH BECOME A PUBLISHED AUTHOR SEE A BLUE WHALE VOLUNTEER AT A SHELTER LEARN TO JUGGLE

It doesn't matter which adventures you choose first—the real adventure, after all, is who you go with.

Simply fill in the following blanks and then trade lists.

I'VE ALWAYS WANTED TO...   **I'VE ALWAYS WANTED TO...**

If you
could open
a door to
anywhere,

where would you go?

GET LOST

Let's go out and let stories happen to us. Let's work them, water them…till they bloom.

~Clarissa Pinkola Estes

See the world. Take your life together and have it everywhere. Stage a five-

course picnic on the Pont Neuf in Paris. Watch sunset tint the domes and

spires of the Taj Mahal. Trace your own path along the ancient stone walls of

Ireland's Aran Islands. Luxuriate in a Turkish bath in Istanbul. Count rainbows at

Zimbabwe's Victoria Falls. Take an old camera, and shoot an entire roll of black

and white film on Easter Island. Mark some choices here. Make a plan. Go there.

These are the days of
miracle and wonder.

~PAUL SIMON

IF YOUR LIFE IS WORTH LIVING, IT'S WORTH RECORDING.

"My boyfriend and I both like to journal. When we first met, we found ourselves reading our personal thoughts, ideas and reflections aloud to each other. It was so interesting to compare the way he perceived a date or experience with the way I perceived the same date or experience with him. **When we moved in together, we decided to create a 'double journal' for the two of us. We keep the journal on the kitchen table so we can both add to it on the fly each day, and we also carry it with us on our adventures.** The journal contains stories from trips we have taken, maps marked with places we have been and want to go, a list of books we want to share, a page of goals we don't want to fall by the wayside, photos and many other little precious writings, reminders, dreams, aspirations and love notes. **Sharing our lives and thoughts in the same book, day by day, with whatever comes to mind adds a whole new dimension, not just to journaling, but to our lives together.**"

Sunday dinners, a three-day weekend, whipped cream and berries, the first morning of spring, music in the park, corn on the cob, a moon on the rise, making breakfast together, hiking, sitting Indian-style at sunrise, wrestling in our pajamas, building a lake cabin with our own hands, taking salsa lessons, waking up on Saturday with no agenda, heading off to nowhere in particular, driving with the music turned up, going on an architectural dig, making plans together, sharing secrets, growing elephant garlic and tomatoes, loving the place we call home, sleeping on our porch, tackling problems together, raising a couple of chickens, offering a shoulder to cry on, giving flowers for no reason, walking at low tide, getting the family together, eating watermelon and watching fireworks, making every moment count.

Cherish Life's Tiny Delights

Eugenia Price once wrote that "The great doing of little things makes the great life." This is especially true if you're with the right person.

If you can close your eyes and see yourselves savoring the little things together, then the future is bright.

In our future, I see us…

How will we make the world a better place?

The needs are great, and none of us ever do great things. But we can do small things, with great love, and together we can do something wonderful.

~Mother Teresa

André Gide once said that our world will be saved by one or two caring people at a time. Some of the most meaningful and important things you will ever do as a couple will be the thoughtful things you do for others.

It can be as simple as taking turns visiting with a lonely neighbor, or as grand as traveling together to Sierra Leone to dig a well for a thirsty village.

As a couple, do you share a passion for photography? Conservation? Gourmet cooking? Music? Why not create a small, medium or large annual scholarship in your name, and give it to a deserving student who shares your passion too?

OR, YOU COULD...

Spend a weekend with Habitat for Humanity, building a house for a needy family.

Volunteer one night a week at a soup kitchen, hospital or animal shelter.

Tutor a child or help coach a youth team in an after-school program, or on weekends.

Volunteer at a senior center to play games, teach crafts, or just sit and talk with a lonely elder.

Wash the dishes, do the shopping, or watch the kids for an evening, so your partner can have a free night to volunteer.

TOGETHER WE CAN DO SOMETHING WONDERFUL...

Here are a few ways we will make a difference in our neighborhood, community, or world:

WHEN A PENNY MEANS MORE THAN A DIAMOND

"You never realize how much your mother loves you," wrote Australian author Pam Brown, "till you explore the attic—and find every letter you ever sent her, every finger painting, clay pot, bead necklace, Easter chicken, cardboard Santa Claus, paper lace Mother's Day card and school report since day one."

Chances are, most of the sentimental gifts you gave to your mother or father as a child cost you next to nothing. But the fact that they came straight from your heart meant everything to your parents.

This same principle applies to the gifts you exchange as a couple. Ask yourself: Which gift means more to your partner—the cashmere sweater that you bought off the rack at the last minute? Or that unusual little seashell you brought back from your romantic getaway at the beach?

In "Chicken Soup for the Romantic Soul" Mrs. B. Bartlett reminisces about the long walks along the railroad tracks that she and her husband used to take when they were young and struggling to make ends meet. In those days they couldn't afford a diamond ring—they could barely afford food and clothing for their children.

One day, while holding hands on their walk, they heard a locomotive approaching from a distance. Her husband dashed up to the railroad tracks and placed a penny on them. That night, he drilled a little hole in the shiny flattened penny and attached it to a charm bracelet, saying, "This is so you'll always remember our walks together."

Her husband died some years ago, but Mrs. Bartlett wrote that she still has that copper penny, and it means more to her than gold or diamonds. "All I have to do is hold my penny in my arthritic hands and I have him and that day all over again."

YOU NEVER KNOW
WHEN YOU'RE MAKING
A MEMORY.

~Rickie Lee Jones

TABLE FOR TWO

Every year, each of us eats about a thousand meals. Together, we can turn many of those meals into something meaningful and memorable—shared time. A single bowl of pasta, with two forks. A spontaneous picnic on a sunny hillside some Sunday afternoon. A potluck housewarming party. With a little thought, a meal together becomes a chance for a special occasion, three times a day.

Food can look beautiful, taste exquisite, smell wonderful, make people feel good, bring them together, inspire romantic feelings.
~Rosamond Richardson

Food is sustenance for the body, but its preparation and enjoyment are sustenance for your relationship. A day spent strolling at the farmer's market among the flowers and vegetables can be a romantic event, but so can an evening walk to the grocery store. A quick and simple breakfast of toast and coffee can be a celebratory meal if you take fifteen minutes to talk and savor it together before you head to work. And when you have a little more time, you can:

Recreate a meal from a favorite restaurant.

Buy a food you've never had before, and learn to cook it together.

Take your favorite sandwiches to a place with a view.

Enroll in a dessert-making class or wine-tasting course.

Try a dish from a part of the world you want to visit.

Make a recipe from your childhood, while you relive your memories of the people you shared it with.

We enjoy early mornings on the porch, fresh corn, going barefoot, blueberries and strawberries and raspberries, sleeping without nightclothes or covers, the long evenings and the texture of the low western sun on fields that are still green. ~Donald M. Murray

Life is an occasion
Make it special.

~Arthur Schopenhauer

You are my inspiration and my folly. You are my light across the sea, my million nameless joys, and my day's wage. You are my divinity, my madness, my selfishness, my transfiguration and purification. You are my rapscallionly fellow vagabond, my tempter and star. I want you.

~GEORGE BERNARD SHAW

You are my...

Say things to the world that are true. ~PABLO CASALS

ARE YOU SOMEONE'S FAVORITE PERSON?

Somewhere there is someone who understands your past, believes in your future, and accepts you today just the way you are. Yours is the name they love most. Your face has been memorized, by touch and by sight. Your birthday is a holiday.

You are the last thing on their mind at night, and the first thing on their mind in the morning. You are the light of their life, and the most valuable player on their team.

Someone keeps the lamp of friendship lit for you, or the home fires burning, or meets you at the airport in the middle of the night, or makes you laugh until your sides ache, or tells you they believe in you before you can even believe in yourself.

What an honor to be loved and appreciated by someone who knows you so well. What a joy if he or she is your favorite person, too.

Somewhere there is someone who dreams of your smile, who finds in your presence that life is worthwhile. So when you are lonely, remember it's true, that somebody somewhere is thinking of you.
~Unknown

"We started off as good friends, and even though we finally fell in love and got married, we still hold our friendship high. Every year on Valentine's Day he sends me two bouquets of flowers instead of one. The first is addressed to the Love of My Life, and the second is addressed to My Best Friend."

Friendship? Yes, please. ~Charles Dickens

If you and your partner have a great friendship, find ways to honor and celebrate it.

WAYS I CAN BE AN EVEN BETTER FRIEND TO THE ONE I LOVE:

_____

_____

_____

_____

_____

_____

_____

It's so much friendlier with two. ~A. A. Milne

I LOVE YOU,

Not only for what you are,

But for what I am

When I am with you.

I LOVE YOU,

Not only for what

You have made of yourself,

But for what

You are making of me.

I LOVE YOU

For the part of me

That you bring out;

I LOVE YOU

For putting your hand

Into my...heart

And passing over

All the foolish, weak things

That you can't help

Dimly seeing there,

And for drawing out

Into the light

All the beautiful belongings

That no one else had looked

Quite far enough to find.

~Roy Croft

Some of the good things you bring out in me.

WHICH IS BETTER: A RELATIONSHIP OR AN AFFAIR?

Actually, the dictionary defines a relationship as "an ongoing state of affairs between two people." So. . .relationships are "affairs." Good relationships are "long term affairs." Great relationships are "long term love affairs." Instead of just a relationship, why not carry on a long-term, never-ending love affair with your partner?

And when you appear

All the rivers sound

In my body, bells

Shake the sky

And a hymn fills the world.

Only you and I,

Only you and I, my love,

Listen to it.

~Pablo Neruda

Ancient Wisdom
The Secret to Great COMMUNICATION

Hundreds of thick, complicated books have been written about the way couples communicate (and the ways they don't communicate.) But one of the oldest and wisest insights is also the shortest. The secret to great communication is conveniently hidden in the word itself. The word "communication" comes from the ancient Latin root word "communicare" which literally means "to unite or share together."

The secret is simple: If whatever you're doing or saying isn't helping you to "unite and share together" as a couple, it's not communication— it's something else.

The more I know you, the more I want to know you more.

~Roy Lessin

To love a person is to learn
the song that is in their heart,
and to sing it to them when
they have forgotten.

~Unknown

Trust is an overworked word,
but one which has special
meaning to those in love.
Like a hug from a child, trust
cannot be demanded; it can
only be earned. Trust grows
with constancy. Trust each
other again and again, and your
love will grow strong and deep.

I trust *you.*

To be loved and trusted
by those who know us
best is life's greatest
compliment.

~Jack Anthony

You can always count on me to: _____

Trust is a
diamond
with many
different facets.

I can always **count on you to:**

Trust is the knowledge that someone will
see you at your best when you feel at your
worst. Trust is the assurance that someone
speaks the world of you when you're out of
the room or out of town. It's knowing that
there will be someone to pick you up from
work, answer the phone when you call, pack
a lunch when you're running late, and play
on your team. Someone you trust knows
your music, sings your song, and backs you
up with harmony. Someone you trust is a
sure shelter, an inspiring word, a hand to
latch onto, a place to call home.

There is a quiet
wind voice inside of me.
It's the same voice
inside of you.
Delicate and persevering,
it led us towards each other.
Across desert sand,
traffic noise, solitary sky.
I found your little house
by the sea. And I
never wanted to leave.

The Persistence of Yellow, № 189,
by Monique Duval

The Language of Love

Can you hear it? Not always, but you can feel it.
Sometimes love speaks to us, not in the usual
or obvious words, but in the subtle language of
touch, feelings, impulses, and gestures.

Couples who love each other can tell each other
a thousand things without talking. A gentle hand
on your shoulder. A smile across the room. A
kiss behind the ear. A stack of fresh wood placed
thoughtfully in the fireplace. These silent little
messages speak volumes.

And so, be generous with the small, sweet acts
that feed the heart and make life special. Woo
each other daily with spontaneous affection. It
can be something as small as bringing a cup of
coffee with just the right amount of their favorite
almond syrup. Or stopping to send a text during
the day to say, "You're in my heart."

LOVE, HONOR AND NEGOTIATE

WOULD YOU RATHER BE RIGHT, OR WOULD YOU RATHER BE HAPPY? IN THE MAD DASH TO PROVE THAT THEY ARE "RIGHT" ABOUT THINGS, ENTIRE NATIONS HAVE GONE TO WAR, BEST FRIENDS HAVE DISSOLVED THEIR FRIENDSHIP, AND COUPLES HAVE PARTED WAYS FOREVER. THIS SEEMS LIKE SOMETHING WE CAN ALL FIX.

QUESTION: IN A HEATED DISCUSSION, WHAT IS YOUR USUAL MOTIVE?

- [ ] **TO BE THE WINNER**
- [ ] **TO SHOW I AM SMARTER**
- [ ] **TO PROVE THAT I AM "RIGHTER" THAN SOMEONE I LOVE**
- [ ] **TO ACKNOWLEDGE EACH OTHER'S POINT OF VIEW AND STAY IN LOVE**

IF YOU AND I LOVE EACH OTHER, WHO REALLY CARES IF I LIKE CHOPIN, AND YOU LIKE COUNTRY–WESTERN? OR IF I LOVE THE MOUNTAINS, AND YOU LOVE THE BEACH? OR IF YOU LOVE A PORTERHOUSE STEAK, AND I LOVE A PORTOBELLO SANDWICH? THINK ABOUT THIS ONE: IF I'M A REPUBLICAN, AND YOU'RE A DEMOCRAT, DOES THAT MEAN THAT I LOVE A DEMOCRAT AND YOU LOVE A REPUBLICAN? IF SO, MAYBE WE'RE ON TO SOMETHING HERE. IN THE END, THE MOST IMPORTANT THING— EVEN MORE THAN BEING RIGHT— IS BEING HAPPY AND IN LOVE.

When people
love each other,
an important
kind of giving
is "giving in."

~Leo Buscaglia

Be a little kinder

than necessary.

Six-Word Love Stories

Some of the most timeless and beautiful thoughts are also the shortest. "God bless America" is just three words, but three are all that's required. Shakespeare's "To thine own self be true" is just six words, but those six words could make a life. The preamble to the Constitution has 52 words, the Gettysburg Address has 271, and the marriage vow has just two.

There's a legend dating back to the 1920's that Ernest Hemingway was challenged to write a complete short story in just six words. According to the legend, Hemingway responded with, "For Sale: Baby Shoes. Never Worn." He said it was among the best things he had ever written.

The editors of *Smith Magazine* applied the Hemingway challenge to the topic of love, and invited people to sum up their romantic life in just six words. Thousands of responses poured in—some filled with happiness, and some with heartbreak. Here are three from well-known personalities:

Much married,
fourth time
is charmed.
Erica Jong

Hired me.
Fired me.
Married me.
Julie Klam

Engaged in
Jerusalem.
Thank you God.
Lynn Harris

And some from the rest of us:

40 years married, 40 more please.

After all that, there he was.

Deaf guy, deaf gal...booom! Love!

Blind Date. Soulmates. Married 65 years.

Years later. Two kids. Still smitten.

Seven dollar wedding. 24 priceless anniversaries.

Childhood Sweethearts, Best Friends, Lovers, Soulmates.

Love never lasted...until I did.

Past gone, future unknown, present bliss.

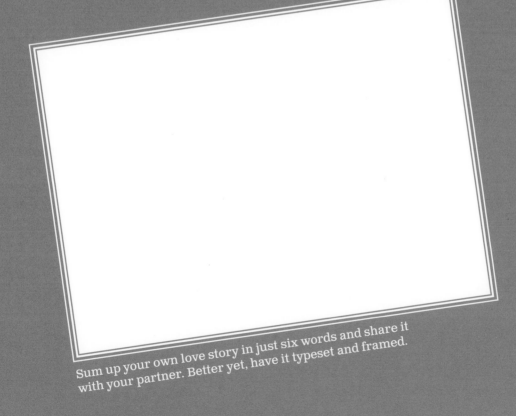

Sum up your own love story in just six words and share it with your partner. Better yet, have it typeset and framed.

WAS THERE SUCH A NIGHT?
IT'S A THRILL I STILL
DON'T QUITE BELIEVE.
BUT AFTER YOU WERE
GONE, THERE WAS
STILL SOME STARDUST
ON MY SLEEVE.

~Johnny Mercer

Remember the place where you first kissed?
Go there and kiss again.

Did you use to meet at the coffee shop by the train station?
Go there and have coffee again.

Did you hold hands at a certain film on one of your first dates?
Rent it and hold hands again.

Remember the year when you first met?
Buy a bottle of wine from that year and toast each other again.

Is there a song or a CD that you played as you fell in love?
When you turn down the sheets tonight, play that song again.

Did you feed each other cake on your wedding day?
The next time you go to a wedding, feed each other cake again.

Remember the hotel where you had your first romantic getaway—or maybe even your honeymoon?
Call and arrange to stay in the same room again.

Has it been awhile since you had some "firsts" with your partner?
Decide that you'll create some new ones today.

RELIVE THE MAGIC

In the blue-collar neighborhood where I grew up lived an old Italian couple named Polly and Menta who loved children, sunflowers, Italian music and each other. Right there in the middle of our concrete city, Polly and Menta had cultivated a lush vegetable garden, complete with hand-split bean poles, trellises, Italian fig trees and tomato plants, two rabbits, three cats, five chickens and a raggedy old rooster that could barely crow. It seems odd now, but the whole neighborhood loved that rooster, and we loved Polly and Menta too. Menta was short and quiet, with big hands, gentle brown eyes, and a perpetual smile. He wore flannel shirts, red long

johns and faded bib overalls year 'round. Polly was taller, straighter and more outgoing than Menta. Like the big yellow sunflowers in their garden, Polly had a sunny disposition that lit up our neighborhood and our lives. She could speak English, too, a skill Menta had always admired but somehow never acquired. It's amazing how much you forget from your childhood. But somewhere in my mind's eye there's a special place that can always picture Polly and Menta working side-by-side in their garden. I can see them putting on their gloves together each morning. Smiling and planning their day. Feeding the birds that came to sing for them. Shooing the cats away from the chickens. Saying grace together over a lunch of fresh beans, tomatoes and onions from the garden, and then dozing and smiling in the afternoon sun, sometimes holding hands.

I remember when our family dog was hit by a car. Polly and Menta knew that my little sister and I were sad. When we walked by their garden on the way home from school, they both called to us. "The rock candy is ripe," shouted Polly, "you should come in and gather some." They led us to a shady corner of the garden, where—sure enough—we found rock candy strewn here and there amongst the real rocks in their garden. Nothing could have raised our spirits more. Years later, when I returned home from college, I decided to go over to Polly and Menta's house early one night. I knew that Menta was growing frail, and I hoped to visit with him if their lights were on. Walking up the alley, I stopped at their gate and looked across the garden to their kitchen window. I could just barely hear a familiar Italian tune playing on their old record player, but I could clearly see Polly and Menta swaying to the music. They had pushed the furniture in the kitchen back a little so they could hold each other in their arms and dance once more. When Menta died that winter, Polly disappeared for weeks. We were sure she'd gone back to the old country. But in the spring, she was back in her garden. Planting sunflowers and vegetables. Feeding the birds that came to sing for her. Shooing the cats away from the chickens. Saying grace over her lunch of fresh beans, tomatoes and onions…and then dozing and smiling in the afternoon sun… probably holding hands.

Lives lived in love can never end.

Grow old
along with me!
The best is
yet to be.

~Robert Browning

WHEN I GET OLDER LOSING MY HAIR,

MANY YEARS FROM NOW.

WILL YOU STILL BE SENDING ME A VALENTINE

BIRTHDAY GREETINGS BOTTLE OF WINE.

When I'm Sixty-Four

IF I'D BEEN OUT 'TIL QUARTER TO THREE

WOULD YOU LOCK THE DOOR,

WILL YOU STILL NEED ME, WILL YOU STILL FEED ME,

WHEN I'M SIXTY-FOUR?

GIVE ME YOUR ANSWER, FILL IN A FORM

MINE FOR EVERMORE

WILL YOU STILL NEED ME, WILL YOU STILL FEED ME,

WHEN I'M SIXTY-FOUR.

~The Beatles

EVERY FRIEND IS TO THE OTHER A SUN, AND A SUNFLOWER ALSO.

Why give a sunflower instead of a rose? True, the red rose is the traditional symbol of love, but the sunflower is the symbol of warmth, happiness, devotion and longevity. Because of the way sunflowers turn their heads toward the sun, anyone who receives a sunflower knows that he or she is the center of the giver's attention.

In the movie, "Calendar Girls" Helen Mirren's character explains...

"I don't think there's anything on this planet that more trumpets life than the sunflower. It's called the sunflower, not because it looks like the sun, but because it follows the sun. During the course of the day, the head of the sunflower tracks the journey of the sun across the sky. Wherever light is, no matter how weak, these flowers will find it. That's such an admirable thing, not just in flowers, but in people— and such a beautiful lesson in life."

Ways you inspire me...

_____

_____

_____

_____

_____

_____

_____

_____

_____

_____

_____

_____

_____

_____

_____

_____

A letter from Civil War Major Sullivan Ballou to his beloved wife, Sarah

At the beginning of the Civil War, Major Sullivan Ballou of the 2nd Rhode Island Infantry wrote a letter to his wife, Sarah. One week later on the plains of Manassas, Virginia, he died fighting at the Battle of Bull Run. Here is a portion of his letter.

14 July 1861

My very dear Sarah:

The indications are very strong that we shall move in a few days—perhaps tomorrow. Lest I should not be able to write again, I feel impelled to write a few lines that may fall under your eye when I shall be no more.

Sarah my love for you is deathless...but if I do not return, never forget how much I love you, and when my last breath escapes me on the battle field, it will whisper your name...

And, O Sarah! if the dead can come back to this earth and flit unseen around those they loved, I shall always be near you; in the gladdest days and in the darkest nights... always, always, and if there be a soft breeze upon your cheek, it shall be my breath; as the cool air fans your throbbing temple, it shall be my spirit passing by.

Sarah do not mourn me dead; think I am gone and wait for thee, for we shall meet again.

It would be a fine

thing, in which I

hardly dare believe,

to pass our lives

near each other,

hypnotized by

our dreams.

~Pierre Curie

Give thanks.

It's important to remember, now and then, that the biggest threat to a couple is not money, incompatibility or even infidelity. The biggest threat, by far, is taking each other for granted.

The way to love and appreciate something even more is simply to realize that it can be lost. Joy is what happens when we recognize how good things really are—right now, today.

"Looking back," wrote David Grayson, "I have only this to regret, that too often when I loved, I did not say so." Tomorrow is promised to no one. Today is always the best day to say, "I appreciate you. You are someone I truly love."

WHAT AM I THANKFUL FOR?

....

....

....

....

....

....

....

....

....

....

....

....

....

WHEN I COUNT
MY BLESSINGS,
I COUNT YOU TWICE.
~Irish Proverb

If you were all alone

in the universe

with no one to talk to,

no one with whom to share

the beauty of the stars,

to laugh with, to touch,

what would be

your purpose in life?

~MITSUGI SAOTOME